GW00385334

...BUT WHOSE IDEA WAS IT?

Eileen Hellicar

David & Charles
Newton Abbot   London   North Pomfret (Vt)

British Library Cataloguing in Publication Data

Hellicar, Eileen
  But whose idea was it?
  1. Inventions—History—Dictionaries
  I. Title
  609   T15

ISBN 0-7153-8474-0

Typeset by Photo-Graphics, Honiton, Devon
and printed in Great Britain by A. Wheaton & Co. Ltd.,
Hennock Road, Exeter
for David & Charles (Publishers) Limited
Brunel House   Newton Abbot   Devon

Published in the United States of America
by David & Charles Inc
North Pomfret Vermont 05053 USA

CONTENTS

INTRODUCTION

How often do you think, when you are eating a favourite food or using a familiar object — 'I wonder who first thought of this? Whose idea was it?'

Who first thought of hot dogs, for instance, or of potato crisps, or of putting a hole in a doughnut? Somebody did — they did not just happen. And whose idea was dry-cleaning, or frozen food, or guide dogs for the blind, or even the inimical parking meter?

These are just a few of the things we now take for granted in our busy modern life. But they all evolved from somebody's idea — and sometimes quite by chance.

Often the person who had the idea is not the person who is credited with the invention. We all know, for example, that Alexander Graham Bell invented the telephone. But it was not his *idea*. That credit goes to a German inventor called Johann Reis, who sadly could not get his project off the ground.

Maybe some things are so mundane that it is hard to believe that they began as an exciting idea in somebody's mind — toilet paper, for instance, or the safety-pin, the escalator, the petrol pump, or the postage stamp.

All the subjects in this book could remain just items and objects of detached familiarity, but I have tried to put them all into a place of interest, to bring them into their own, by showing who it was who first brought them into existence, and how the idea became the familiar object that we know today.

Eileen Hellicar
Mitcham

4

AEROSOL CAN
Erik Rotheim · 1926

The aerosol can was the idea of a Norwegian engineer named Erik Rotheim, who developed his invention in 1926.

Rotheim discovered that if he introduced a liquid or gas — such as Freon — into a can, internal pressure could be created which would propel a product from the can in a fine spray.

But the aerosol was not developed for commercial use until 1941 when two American chemists, Goodhue and Sullivan, produced an insect spray.

ANTISEPSIS
Ignaz Philipp Semmelweis · 1847

The need for antisepsis in hospitals was first recognised by Ignaz Semmelweis, the nineteenth-century Hungarian obstetrician.

In 1847, while Semmelweis was working in a lying-in hospital in Vienna, he noticed that deaths from puerperal fever were three times as high in women who had been attended by doctors and students who had come straight from post-mortem rooms, than in those who had been attended by midwives. Semmelweis deduced that the deaths were due to septic matter carried on the hands of the doctors, and he introduced a system of disinfecting the hands with a solution of chlorinated lime.

Although the hand cleansing reduced the death rate considerably, Semmelweis encountered much opposition to his methods, and instead of gaining recognition among his fellow doctors, they were derided and forgotten until after his death in 1865.

Twenty years after Semmelweis's discovery, Joseph Lister introduced antisepsis into surgery with the use of carbolic acid. But Lister had advantages unknown to Semmelweis — notably Pasteur's theory of germ-disease — and so did not meet the same annihilating opposition.

The natural progression from antisepsis was asepsis — the exclusion of bacteria from surgical procedures — which in modern surgery is fortunately taken for granted.

BABY INCUBATOR
Alexandre Lion · 1891

The idea of the incubator cabinet for the intensive care of premature and weak babies came from a French doctor, Alexandre Lion of Nice, in 1891.

Dr Lion based his invention on the principles of the coal-fired egg-hatching incubator designed in 1609 by the Dutch physicist, Cornelius Drebbel. The air in Dr Lion's incubator was purified through a filter and kept fresh by means of a fan ventilator. The temperature was regulated automatically by a thermostat. Babies who were too weak to swallow were fed through the nose by means of a specially shaped spoon.

Soon after his invention, with which Dr Lion saved the lives of several babies, he opened a clinic specially for incubated babies at Nice. There, during the first three years, he claimed a success rate of 72 per cent of all babies placed in his incubators. Later, clinics were opened in Paris, Lyons, Bordeaux and Marseilles. In Paris the public were allowed to view the incubated babies for 50 centimes — the money collected helped to pay the nurses' salaries and other expenses incurred at the clinic.

In 1897, Dr Lion's incubator was introduced to London.

BALLPOINT PEN
John H. Loud · 1888

The idea of using a rotating ball to deliver ink from a pen was first conceived by an American, John H. Loud, in 1888. Loud's pen was chiefly designed for marking rough surfaces, such as canvas, and although he patented his idea, the pen was never used for writing. Its failure was probably due to the fact that Loud used a pad soaked in ordinary ink to supply the ball and this, of course, blotted as the ball rotated.

Loud's idea probably inspired the wheel-point pen. But this also failed for the same reason — that the ink blotted.

Then, in the 1930s, a Hungarian journalist, Ladislao Biro, became interested in the quick-drying ink used by printers, and wondered if the quick-drying process could be applied to ink for writing. He devised a pen on the ballpoint principle, using ink made from a mixture of sulphate and iron and gallnuts, which did not blot.

Biro applied for a patent in 1938. But in 1939, before the patent was granted, he was fleeing the Nazis at the outbreak of World War II. He went to Paris, then to Spain, and eventually to Buenos Aires, where with his brother George, a chemist, he perfected his ballpoint. In 1944 Biro sold his invention to one of his financial backers, an Englishman named Henry Martin. Martin then produced the pen for the British and American forces to aid the war effort. The ballpoint was a boon to the forces for it could be used both at high altitudes and under water without leaking.

Eventually the pen was sold to the French company of BiC which now produces more than 12 million pens per day throughout the world. Although 'Biro' is almost synonymous with ballpoint, the inventor received little reward for his invention and despite the regular use of his name Biro himself sank into obscurity in Buenos Aires.

BINGO
Edwin Lowe · 1923

The game of bingo, which now occupies the leisure hours of millions of people, came about quite by accident.

One day in 1923 Edwin Lowe, an American salesman, was watching a game called Beano being played at a carnival in Atlanta, Georgia. He became fascinated by the people placing little beans on a correct number, and bought some of the hand-printed cards and a box of little numbered discs, so that he could introduce the game to his family and friends. The game soon caught on at community events and one evening as Lowe was calling out the numbers, excitement grew as the participants waited for the last number. Finally a young woman placed her last bean on her card and screamed 'Bingo' — instead of 'Beano'. Lowe said afterwards that he experienced a strange sense of elation when the girl shrieked the wrong word, and he determined then and there to come out with a game called Bingo.

Very soon Lowe had produced a twenty-four-card Bingo kit which he sold for two dollars. But Lowe realised the snag when a priest, who had organised a Bingo night to raise money for his church, complained that with only twenty-four cards there were too many winners in a single game. He suggested to Lowe that more numerical combinations were needed.

Not relishing the task of thinking up sequences of numbers that did not repeat, Lowe hired Professor Carl Lefler, a mathematician from Columbia University, to do the job for him. Lefler was commissioned to produce 6,000 different cards. Despite increasing difficulty as the cards mounted up, Lefler persevered, and eventually the task was finished. But so was Lefler, for it left him insane.

BOY SCOUTS
Robert Baden-Powell · 1907

The Boy Scout movement began with a 10-day camp, held at Brownsea Island, Poole, Dorset in 1907. The camp, which ran from 29 July to 9 August, was organised by Lieutenant-General Robert Baden-Powell, who gathered together twenty boys to try out his idea of a 'Game of Scouting'. The boys, nine of whom were from the local Boys' Brigade companies, the others sons of Baden-Powell's friends, formed themselves into four groups, or patrols — the Wolves, Curlews, Bulls and Ravens — and followed an organised set of activities such as knot-tying, cooking, observation and physical exercises.

Baden-Powell's intention was not so much to found a national organisation as to provide boys with the chance to learn the skills that he had learned as a soldier while serving in various parts of the world. But scouting caught on when Baden-Powell published his twice-monthly partwork, *Scouting for Boys*. Boys from all over the country formed themselves into groups to follow his guidance.

The first recognised Scout Troop was the 1st Glasgow, founded by Robert Young, which dates from January 1908. Close on their heels came troops from Nottingham, Sunderland and Hampstead.

On 7 October 1922 the Boy Scouts of Britain were the recipients of the first Royal broadcast, when the Prince of Wales (later Edward VIII), who was their royal patron, addressed them from York House on the occasion of the National Scout Rally at Alexandra Palace. Today Scouting is a world-wide movement, and with its millions of members it is the largest international voluntary secular organisation in the world.

BRASSIÈRE
Mary Phelps Jacob · 1914

Today's modern liberated young women may not be grateful to Mary Phelps Jacob, but the tightly-laced corseted belles at the time of World War I certainly were. Yet, ironically, Mary, a wealthy New York débutante, paved the way for today's liberation.

In 1914 the nineteen-year-old Mary struck a note for freedom. Tiring of her hour-glass figure, which was shaped by tightly-laced whalebone corsets, she rebelled against convention and cast aside her restricting nether garments. In their place she wore a little lightweight contraption that she had made herself by stitching two lace handkerchiefs on to a piece of pale pink ribbon. Her lightly supported and gently revealed figure made the stunning socialite even more the belle of the New York scene. And soon her envious friends were asking her to sew brassières for them.

Mary then applied for a patent and set about marketing her invention. But her business brain could not compete with her inventive brain. Her efforts were not successful, and she sold her patent to the Warner Brothers Corset Company for $15,000 (£3,750). And Warners have never regretted their buy, for over the years the brassière has earned them millions of pounds.

CARPET SWEEPER
Melville Bissell · 1876

An allergy to sawdust and straw prompted Melville Bissell, a prosperous Michigan businessman, to invent the carpet sweeper in 1876.

Bissell, the owner of a crockery shop in Grand Rapids, Michigan, suddenly became allergic to the sawdust and straw that was packed around his china-ware. His allergy took the form of headaches, which became increasingly worse with each new delivery. Each item he unpacked sent Bissell into a paroxysm of agony as he breathed in the dust which scattered from the straw that was protecting his precious chinaware.

Bissell's problem was to find a way to remove the dust before he breathed it in, and each night when his shop closed he experimented with ideas, until at last he came up with the idea of a hand-operated sweeper with an enclosed rotating brush.

Bissell patented his invention and in September 1876 he opened the Bissell Carpet Sweeper Company to produce his labour-saving sweepers. The company prospered and in the 1950s Bissell's grandson introduced the first carpet shampooing machine.

From those early days of an idea born out of necessity, Bissell's invention, little changed from its original design, now sells in millions throughout the world.

CASH REGISTER
James J. Ritty · 1879

It was a fiddling barman who provoked the first cash register. During the latter part of the nineteenth century, James Ritty ran a popular saloon in Dayton, Ohio. Despite increasingly successful business his profits never seemed to increase. This bothered Ritty to such an extent that he worked himself into a nervous breakdown and was ordered by his doctor to take a long sea voyage to recuperate.

Ritty boarded a liner for Europe. During the voyage he visited the ship's engine-room, and that voyage not only cured his nervous breakdown, but also cured his falling profits. For in the engine-room Ritty saw a device that counted the revolutions of the ship's propellers. The idea then struck him that the same mechanical principle could be used for registering business transactions.

When he returned from his trip he put the idea to his brother John, a mechanic. Together they contrived a metal device that looked rather like a clock, with two rows of keys beneath it. The clock face had two rings of figures — cents on the outer ring and dollars on the inner ring — and a large hand for indicating cents, and a small hand which pointed to dollars. The two rows of keys, each with a number printed on it, controlled the hands. If the $2 key was pressed, the small hand moved to number 2 on the inner circle. Similarly, if the 2 cents key was pressed the large hand moved to number 2 on the outer circle. Inside the machine were two discs which added up the total of sales that were registered.

The Ritty brothers' cash register was patented on 4 November 1879, and thereafter the popular saloon began to show the profit it earned.

CAT'S EYES
Percy Shaw · 1934

The eyes of a cat, gleaming through thick fog, saved a motorist from disaster, and gave him the idea for an invention that made him a millionaire.

In 1933 Percy Shaw, a Yorkshire road contractor, was driving in thick fog along a country lane between Bradford and Halifax. The sight of a cat's eyes reflected in his car's headlights made him jam on the brakes in the nick of time before his car left the road. He found that the cat was sitting on a wall overlooking a sheer drop.

This terrifying experience gave Shaw the idea that pinpricks of light, resembling the cat's eyes, carefully placed along the road would aid driving in the dark. Shaw experimented for a year, and then produced his reflecting studs which cleaned themselves.

He patented his idea in 1934, and in that year the first studs were laid in a road near Bradford. The following year, Shaw opened a factory to manufacture his studs, which became known as cat's eyes.

Each stud has two pairs of eyes — a pair facing in each direction — mounted in a domed rubber pad which is sunk in the road. Each eye, a carefully designed prism with a sealed, aluminium mirror behind it, directs incoming light back along its path. As passing traffic depresses the stud, the prism is wiped clean by the inside of the rubber dome.

Cat's eyes were a boon during the blackout of World War II, since the reflected light was not thrown upwards. Shaw was awarded the OBE for his contribution to road safety, but his fame and fortune did not change his way of life. He continued to live in his native Halifax, contending that Yorkshire provided all that he wanted in life.

CELLOPHANE
Jacques Edwin Brandenberger · 1908

Cellophane was first made by a Swiss chemist named Jacques Brandenberger in 1908.

Brandenberger made his discovery by dissolving wood pulp in cellulose and forcing the sticky result through a narrow opening into a bath of acid.

CELLULOID
John Wesley Hyatt · 1908

In 1908 the American inventor, John Hyatt, experimented by mixing camphor with cellulose-nitrate. The result was a plastic material, which he named celluloid.

CHRISTMAS CARD
Sir Henry Cole · 1843

Every Christmas Sir Henry Cole would write to his friends to wish them the compliments of the season. But as Christmas 1843 drew near, Sir Henry found that pressure of business was preventing him from following his usual custom. He did not want his friends to go unremembered so he asked the artist John Calcott Horsley to design a card for him that he could have printed and send out to all his friends.

Horsley's card, which measured 5in × 3¼in, showed a Victorian family sitting round the Christmas table, raising their glasses to the absent friend. And this seemingly harmless scene caused a furore among temperance societies who thought that the wine-drinking family encouraged drunkenness and bawdiness. Nevertheless, 1,000 cards were printed by Jobbins of Holborn, and those in excess of Cole's and Horsley's requirements were sold in a shop in Bond Street for one shilling each.

But the sending of cards did not catch on immediately, and although other designs are known to have been printed in following years, Christmas cards did not become commercially successful until about 1871.

CHRISTMAS CRACKERS
Tom Smith · 1840s

Christmas crackers, which today are taken for granted as part of Christmas festivities, were the brainchild of Tom Smith, a London baker and confectioner. But they evolved in a very circuitous fashion.

In early Victorian England, when Tom Smith ran his shop, sweets were sold unwrapped in little paper bags. While on a visit to France, Smith noticed that sweets, or bon-bons as they are called in France, were wrapped in coloured paper, with twisted ends. Tom Smith brought the idea back to his London shop, but was disappointed that his wrapped sweets did not outsell the unwrapped ones. He then thought of tucking little love-mottoes inside the wrapper to encourage sales. But still his customers were not interested.

Smith took his idea even further, and began to wrap up little novelties and toys in coloured paper with twisted ends. But again, his customers were not as interested in them as he had hoped they would be.

Then, as Smith was poking the log fire in his drawing-room one Christmas morning, the smouldering log suddenly blazed up with a shower of sparks that crackled and cracked. And Smith hit upon his idea. He would introduce a 'bang' into his wrapped novelties. After months of experimenting, he discovered how to treat two pieces of paper so that they would produce a little 'snap' when pulled apart.

This idea did not fail. Smith's bon-bons, as they were originally called, comprised a toy, a motto and a treated piece of paper wrapped in brightly coloured paper with twisted ends. When pulled, the bon-bon exploded and the 'treasures' were revealed.

Tom Smith then patented his idea and around the mid-1840s founded a company to manufacture his brainwave. Today more than 3 million boxes of crackers are sold each Christmas.

COCA-COLA
Dr John Pemberton · 1886

The dark brown soft drink, known the world over as 'Coke', was invented by Dr John Pemberton of Atlanta, Georgia, in 1886.

Dr Pemberton, a pharmacist, used to make patent medicines with fancy names such as Globe Flower Cough Syrup and Extract of Styllinger, which his customers bought to cure their minor ailments. Then one day Dr Pemberton experimented with essences and oils, which he mixed with extracts of cola nuts and coca leaves in a stone pot in his back yard. He was hoping to find a cure for hangovers, but he came up with a very pleasant-tasting concoction. He added carbonated water to his syrup and took it down to the local soda-fountain where it was sold for five cents a glass.

The new drink, which Dr Pemberton's partner, Frank Robinson, had christened Coca-Cola, did not sell as well as Pemberton had hoped. Only twenty-five gallons were sold in the first year. The following year, disappointed and in need of money because of ill health, Dr Pemberton sold most of his shares in his invention to two friends for little more than 200 dollars. In February 1888 — four months before he died — he sold the remaining shares to a businessman, Asa Candler, for 500 dollars.

By 1892 Candler owned all the shares in Coca-Cola and decided the way to sell his product was to advertise it. In January 1893 he registered the trademark 'Coca-Cola' and churned the drink out by the barrel-load. Coca-Cola signs appeared in every possible place.

Demand grew at the soda fountains, and in 1899 two men, Benjamin Thomas and Joseph Whitehead — baseball fans who saw the advantages of providing Coke at baseball matches and other gatherings where there were no soda-fountains — obtained from Candler the exclusive rights to bottle and sell the drink. The bottlers soon made themselves a fortune and Candler became a multimillionaire. In 1919 he sold his company to an Atlanta banker, Ernest Woodruff, for 25 million dollars.

Coke continued to be phenomenally popular, and in 1926 Woodruff established a foreign sales department and the drink started its climb to its present-day sales record of more than 250 million Cokes being consumed each day in more than 135 countries throughout the world.

Coke is still made from the same recipe that Dr Pemberton concocted in his backyard in the days of Queen Victoria. And that recipe is still one of the most closely guarded secrets in the world, being known only to two or three 'trusties' of the Coke empire.

COMPUTER
Charles Babbage · 1834

Although the computer is thought of as an accepted part of modern life, the idea came from a Victorian mathematician and inventor, Charles Babbage, who was born at Totnes in Devon.

Babbage, who some ten years earlier had invented an advanced calculator that could multiply and divide as well as add and subtract, visualised a machine that could perform any calculation he put into it. In 1834 he made the first drawings of his 'Analytical Engine', as he called it. But although he spent the next fifty years trying to perfect it, the machine, which consisted of hundreds of gear wheels, was beyond the capabilities of Victorian technology and it was never finished.

Babbage had worked out a system whereby punched cards containing information and instructions would pass through a device that would 'read' the information and calculate the answer, which would then be printed out. As in a modern computer the calculations were processed individually by a mechanism that Babbage called a mill. The information on the cards and the calculations provided in the answer would be stored in a memory section.

Babbage's dream lay virtually dormant for almost a hundred years. Then in the 1940s electronic computers began to be made and the term 'electronic brain' came into use. The first general purpose electronic computer — the ENIAC (Electronic Numerical Integrator and Calculator) — was completed at the University of Pennsylvania in 1945. This was an enormous contraption employing 18,000 thermionic valves, weighing 30 tons and occupying enough space to house hundreds of modern models. It was programmed by plugging in leads.

From those early beginnings the computer is accessible to everybody and has become as much a part of life as the telephone or television set.

CONSERVATIVE PARTY
Sir Robert Peel · 1834

When Robert Peel was asked to become Prime Minister on the dismissal of Lord Melbourne in November 1834, he immediately dissolved Parliament and went to the country. Peel, who was against parliamentary reform, made his famous speech to his constituents at Tamworth saying that although the Reform Act — which had been passed in June 1832 — must be accepted, the government would be conservative and retain what was good of the old ways.

This speech became known as the Tamworth Manifesto, and from it was born the Conservative Party as opposed to the old Tories.

CORRUGATED IRON
Richard Walker · 1828

In 1828 Richard Walker, a builder from London, realised that he could strengthen his building materials by making them wavy.

He opened a factory to make his new material, but his task was laborious as each corrugation was put in individually.

In 1844 a Birmingham engineer, named John Spencer, patented his idea of shaped rollers to make the corrugations.

CROSSWORD PUZZLE
Arthur Wynne · 1913

In December 1913 Arthur Wynne, the English editor of the *New York World*'s Sunday supplement magazine, *Fun*, was looking for something original for his Christmas issue. Recalling a parlour game called magic square, which he used to play with his grandfather as a child in Liverpool, he devised a word cross — a diamond shaped frame with a blacked out, cross-shaped centre, containing thirty-two simple clues. The puzzle was an immediate success and Wynne went on to devise another puzzle in a square frame, with numbered clues and blacked out squares, which was re-named the crossword.

So successful was Wynne's idea that other newspapers followed suit and soon the crossword craze began.

One compiler, Robert Stilgenbauer of Los Angeles, spent eleven years, from 1938 until 1949, compiling the longest crossword ever published. It contained 2,008 vertical clues and 2,007 horizontal ones. But so far, despite more than 125,000 copies being distributed, no one has reportedly completed it.

DETERGENT
August Beychler · 1913

Although we think of detergents as very much a part of modern living, they were in fact first thought of as early as 1913 by a Belgian chemist named August Beychler.

The first detergent was a product called Nekal, which was produced in Germany in 1917 to relieve the soap shortage during World War I.

DISHWASHER
Mrs W.A. Cockran · 1889

Not surprisingly, perhaps, the idea for the dishwasher came from a woman — Mrs W.A. Cockran, a housewife from Indiana.

The story goes that Mrs Cockran took ten years to build her machine since her husband, a wealthy businessman, would not help her financially to pursue her 'crazy idea'. And it was not until he died that her friends rallied round with financial gifts and loans and she was able to produce her first model, in 1889.

Mrs Cockran's machine consisted of a wooden tub containing a removable wire basket on which the dishes were stacked. Water was sprayed over the dishes by a pump operated by turning a handle on the outside of the tub. Rollers at the bottom of the tub revolved to turn the dishes. Later, larger machines were driven by a steam engine.

A contemporary newspaper report describing Mrs Cockran's machine said that it was capable of 'washing, scalding, rinsing and drying up to two dozen dishes of all shapes and sizes in two minutes'.

The dishwasher soon caught on in America, and thanks to Mrs Cockran the irksome chore of washing up became a thing of the past for many people. It was to be many years before the labour-saving device crossed the Atlantic to Britain but, like many other one-time luxuries, it is fast becoming one of the necessities of life.

19

DRY-CLEANING
Jean-Baptiste Jolly · 1855

As with the telephone (see page 53), dry-cleaning came into existence as the result of a man spilling a chemical on to his clothes.

In 1855 Frenchman Jean-Baptiste Jolly spilled camphene — a chemical rather like turpentine — on to his jacket. But his horror turned to surprise when he found that instead of being ruined, the jacket had a clean patch on it.

This discovery prompted Jolly to commercialise his happy find and open a dry-cleaning business. At first it was a dangerous business, for the cleaning solvents were highly inflammable agents such as benzine, paraffin and gasoline. But over the years safer solvents have been discovered, and careful study and experimentation by chemists and mechanical engineers has made dry-cleaning harmless to even the most delicate fabrics.

Dry-cleaning came to Britain about 1860 and has since spread to most countries throughout the world. Which is just as well since, during normal wear, a garment picks up about two ounces of dust and dirt in six months.

ELECTROMAGNET
William Sturgeon · 1820

In 1820 William Sturgeon, a self-educated English electrical engineer and son of a shoemaker, became interested in the recent discovery of the Danish physicist, Hans Christian Oersted, that there was a link between electricity and magnetism. Oersted made his discovery when he held a compass close to an electrified wire, and the wire activated the compass needle.

Sturgeon took this discovery a step further. He wound a length of wire round a horseshoe-shaped piece of iron and passed an electric current through it — thus making what he called an electromagnet, capable of lifting twenty times its own weight.

Ten years later, Sturgeon's magnet was improved upon by Joseph Henry, the American physicist. Henry wound a piece of silk-insulated copper wire, layer upon layer, round an iron bar, and this greatly increased the magnet's power. By using a battery Henry made one of his magnets lift 750lb, and another 2,086lb.

The electromagnet has since been used in countless electrical inventions including the telephone, transformer and dynamo.

William Sturgeon also devised the moving-coil galvanometer and built the first successful rotary electric motor based on the principles of Michael Faraday.

ESCALATOR
Jesse W. Reno · 1894

The escalator was the brainchild of American entrepreneur Jesse Reno, and was first used in 1894 as a joy ride on the Coney Island pier, in New York.

Reno's inclined elevator, as he called it, consisted of a conveyor belt pulling an articulated ramp at an angle of 30°. Obviously New Yorkers preferred to ride rather than walk, for in 1896 four escalators were installed in Siegel Cooper's department store in Manhattan. Two years later one was installed in Harrods store in London.

Very soon escalators were installed in the subways to bring passengers to and from the street, the first being used at the 3rd Avenue station of the Elevated Railway in New York City. In 1911 London's Underground installed one at Earl's Court station, where the 80ft rise was for many years the world's highest.

In 1911 Reno sold his company to the Otis Elevator Company, who owned the rights to another type of escalator design. By 1920 Otis had combined the best features of both designs, and produced a moving staircase with moving handrail which travelled at 90ft per minute.

Today in the USA more than 14,000 escalators carry 30,000 million people every year, at a speed of 120ft per minute.

FINGERPRINTS
William Herschel · 1877

Fingerprinting was first used in 1877 by William Herschel, as a means of preventing crime rather than detecting it.

Herschel, a member of the Indian Civil Service in Hooghly, West Bengal, made the Army pensioners leave their fingerprints when they drew their pensions to ensure that they did not try to draw the money a second time.

In 1892 the scientist Sir Francis Galton published his *Finger Prints*, which showed how he had improved upon Herschel's technique. In 1895 he published a further work, *Finger Print Directories*, which drew attention to the usefulness of fingerprinting.

Later, Sir Edward Henry, Chief Commissioner of the Metropolitan Police, devised a system for classifying fingerprints, which was generally adopted. In 1901 Scotland Yard opened its fingerprint division under the direction of Sir Edward.

FROZEN FOOD
Clarence Birdseye · 1924

The idea of freezing food is accredited to Clarence Birdseye, an American biologist and fur trader.

During the years between 1912 and 1915 Birdseye was working on a United States government survey of fish and wildlife in Labrador. Whilst there he watched the natives catching fish which, in the sub-zero temperatures, froze stiff as soon as they were taken out of the water. Months later when they were thawed out the fish were still fresh and had not lost their flavour. The Eskimos also introduced Birdseye to frozen cabbages and caribou meat.

Birdseye was intrigued, for he knew that normal methods of freezing fish or meat created large ice crystals that burst the cell walls, so producing a tasteless, soggy mass when thawed. Birdseye decided that with quick freezing, as in the natural sub-zero temperatures of the Arctic, the tissues must freeze almost instantly, without the formation of ice crystals that affected the cell structure. Birdseye then spent many months trying to puzzle out nature's secret.

When he returned from the Arctic, Birdseye bought himself the basic equipment of brine, ice and an electric fan, and continued to experiment. Eventually he found the method of instant freezing — exposing fresh food to a circulating mist of brine at 45° below zero.

Birdseye patented his idea and in 1924 he set up the General Seafoods Corporation at Gloucester, Massachusetts. He froze peas, spinach, raspberries and other fruit, as well as meats and fish.

In 1929 he sold his patents and his fast-freezing plant for $22 million to the Postum Company. The company adopted Birdseye's name, split into two words, as their brand name. In 1945 Unilever acquired the patents for the British market, and today more than £1,000 million worth of frozen food is sold in Britain each year.

GUIDE DOG
Dr Gorlitz · 1916

It was the sensible action of an Alsatian dog that led Dr Gorlitz, Director of the Frauendorf Sanatorium in Stettin, Poland, to think of training dogs to help the blind.

One day in 1916, Dr Gorlitz was walking in the grounds of the sanatorium with a partially paralysed German officer, whom he used to take for remedial walks. During the walk, Dr Gorlitz was called away, and the officer tried to make his own way back to the building. Watching him was the doctor's Alsatian dog, Excelsior, who immediately turned into the sanatorium, brought out the paralysed man's walking stick and took it over to him. When Dr Gorlitz returned, he saw Excelsior carefully leading the stumbling officer back to the building.

Dr Gorlitz then thought that dogs of such superior intelligence should be able to be trained to give the same assistance to blind people.

That same year, dogs began to be trained by the Austrian War Dog Institute and by the German Association for Serving Dogs. At the end of World War I a permanent training centre was set up under government auspices at Potsdam. In July 1931 the Guide Dog movement was begun in Britain at Wallasey in Cheshire.

HELL-FIRE CLUB
Sir Francis Dashwood · 1755

One of the eighteenth-century's most irreverent organisations, the Hell-fire Club, was founded by Sir Francis Dashwood in 1755.

Dashwood, well known as a practical joker, formed his club from members of a political clique known as the King's Friends — the Tory opposition party bent on ousting the Whigs. Among the twenty-four members were the Earl of Sandwich, John Wilkes and the poet Paul Whitehead. The club's motto was *Fay ce que voudras*, 'Do what you will', and the members, the Monks of Medmenham as they were called, held black masses and mock religious ceremonies in the ruined Cistercian Abbey at Medmenham, which was part of Dashwood's estate. They also held orgies and black magic rituals in caves which Sir Francis had had cut into the hillside opposite West Wycombe Park, his home in Buckinghamshire.

The club, whose official title was the Society of St Francis of Wycombe, broke up in 1763 when Dashwood let loose a baboon as Lord Sandwich was conducting a ceremony invoking the devil. Members thought the devil himself had appeared and fled in terror.

Despite his practical jokes and weird sense of humour, Dashwood was an intelligent, caring man and an able politician. With his great friend, Benjamin Franklin, he produced a shortened version of the *Book of Common Prayer* to help the old and sick who could not 'remain for hours in a cold church'. This version was later used as the basis of the American Episcopalian prayer book.

THE HOLE IN THE DOUGHNUT

Hanson Crockett Gregory · 1847

Nowhere in the world is the doughnut such an institution as it is in the United States of America. And so it is not surprising that it was an American who invented the doughnut's hole.

In 1847 fifteen-year-old Hanson Crockett Gregory, who lived in Clam Cove, Maine, was watching his mother cook the family's favourite 'fried cakes', as doughnuts were then called. When Mama Gregory tossed the sizzling cookies on to a plate, young Hanson exclaimed that the centres had not cooked as well as the outsides. 'But they never do get quite done,' his mother told him. The boy then took a knife and gouged a hole through the middle of each cake, saying, 'Then let's do away with the centres.' And so the doughnut with the hole was born.

Young Hanson grew up to be an intrepid merchant navy captain, and the doughnut with the hole spread throughout the world. And to celebrate the centenary of the hole, a bronze plaque was placed on the Gregory home where it was born.

Various other accounts have been put forward over the years as to the hole's origin, including a claim by Chief High Eagle, a Wampanoag Indian, that the hole was the invention of one of his ancestors. But in October 1941, the National Dunking Association of America denied all other versions and confirmed the fifteen-year-old Hanson Gregory as the hole's inventor.

HOT DOGS
Antoine Feuchtwanger · 1880s

In the mid-1880s a Bavarian immigrant called Antoine
Feuchtwanger set up a small stand in a street in St Louis
in the USA and introduced frankfurter sausages to
America. At first, Feuchtwanger had a problem serving
the sausages because he could not afford plates and
forks, and his customers could not hold the hot sausages in their fingers. Feuchtwanger offered a pair of
gloves with each sausage, but this did not last long as
too many people pocketed the gloves when they had
finished the frankfurter.

Then Feuchtwanger hit upon the simple, but money-
spinning idea of placing the sausage in a sliced open roll
— and the 'hot dog' was born, although the popular
name came some twenty years later.

One day in April 1900, Harry Stevens, who ran the
frankfurter stalls at the New York Polo Ground, in-
structed his salesmen to shout: 'They're hot, red hot.
Get your dachshund sausages while they're hot.'

Hearing the call, Tad Dorgan, a newspaper cartoonist, was inspired to draw a cartoon of two frankfurters,
wrapped in their protective rolls, barking at each other.
Dorgan, who apparently could not spell dachshund,
entitled his cartoon 'hot dogs' — and hot dogs they
have been ever since.

HYPODERMIC SYRINGE
Charles Gabriel Pravaz · 1850

A French surgeon, Charles Gabriel Pravaz, used the
hypodermic syringe in about 1850 to inject medicines
beneath the skin of his patients.

This way the treatment had a quicker effect than
when given by mouth.

JACK
Villard de Honnecourt · 1250

The French architect, Villard de Honnecourt, designed the first screw-jack in about 1250.

De Honnecourt saw its potential as a means of lifting and holding heavy objects during the process of building.

JAZZ BAND
Buddy Bolden · c. 1900

The first recognised jazz band was formed in New Orleans at the turn of the century by a Negro musician named Buddy Bolden. The band was made up of a trumpet — played by Buddy himself — a clarinet, trombone, cornet, guitar, violin, string bass and drums. Buddy is said to have got his idea for his music from the negro spirituals he heard in church as a boy, ragtime and march tunes. Combining the rhythms of these three styles, Buddy produced a distinctive rhythm from which pure jazz was to evolve.

Buddy Bolden's band played on in New Orleans for about seven years, until in 1907 its leader became insane and was sent to an asylum.

In 1915 the first jazz orchestration was published. This was Jelly Roll Morton's 'Jelly Roll Blues', composed in 1905. Jelly Roll, who believed he was the inventor of jazz, also claimed to be the originator of the word 'jazz'.

The first jazz band to play in Britain was the Original Dixieland Jazz Band, comprising cornet, trombone, clarinet, piano and drums, which arrived from the United States to appear at the London Hippodrome in the variety show *Joy Bells*. They played just one stand, on 7 April 1919, as the star of the show, George Robey felt he was being upstaged by them and demanded that they go immediately. They were soon re-engaged to play five days later at the London Palladium. And subsequently performed in various clubs and dance halls throughout Britain.

JIG-SAW PUZZLE
John Spilsbury · 1763

The patience-consuming task of forming a picture from hundreds of scrambled pieces was the idea of John Spilsbury, an eighteenth-century English engraver and map-maker.

Spilsbury began by pasting his maps on to lengths of wood, which he then cut into little odd-shaped pieces that could be fitted easily together. He called his idea 'dissected maps', and very soon schools were buying them as a means of teaching children geography.

From this educational beginning in 1763, puzzles began to be made for pleasure. Eventually they were cut from cardboard, which was easier to handle and cheaper than wood.

The name jig-saw puzzle was thought up in America, where a jig-saw was used to cut the pieces.

LAUNDERETTE
J.F. Cantrell · 1934

The launderette was the idea of J.F. Cantrell of Fort Worth, Texas.

On 18 April 1934 Cantrell opened his 'Washateria' with four electric washing machines in a shop in Fort Worth. Customers were charged for use of the machines by the hour.

The first launderette in Britain was opened at Queensway, London, by Bendix Home Appliances on 9 May 1949.

MATCHES
John Walker · 1827

One day in 1827 John Walker, an English chemist, was mixing the chemicals antimony sulphide and potassium chlorate in a glass container in his pharmacy at Stockton-on-Tees. His mixing finished, he bent down to scrape his mixing stick on the stone floor to clean it — and to his amazement it burst into flames. It was then that John Walker got his idea for matches.

Until that time candles and lamps, which were the only means of lighting, were lit by a flame carried from the fire, or by a spark caused by striking a flint against a piece of metal. Walker began to make cardboard 'lighters' to sell in his shop. And he sold them under the name of 'lucifers' — light bearers. The lighters were packed in tin tubes and sold for one shilling a hundred matches.

Very soon Walker began to make wooden matches. They were little splinters of pinewood tipped with a mixture of antimony sulphide, potassium chlorate and gum arabic, and were ignited by being drawn rapidly through a piece of folded sandpaper. Great effort was often needed to ignite the matches. Then, four years later, Dr Charles Sauria of France invented his 'strike anywhere' match, using both phosphorus and potassium chlorate in the tipping composition. Unfortunately the fumes from the phosphorus had such an adverse effect upon the factory workers that its use was rendered illegal by the international treaty of Berne in 1906, and by the British Parliament.

Today the manufacture of matches is a highly mechanised operation and millions of boxes are sold each year throughout the world.

MECCANO
Frank Hornby · 1906

Frank Hornby was a Liverpool meat importer and the father of two young sons. He was also a very competent amateur engineer with a well-equipped home workshop. It so peeved him to watch his two young sons discard their toys once the initial interest and pleasure had passed that he thought how much better it would be if children could dismantle their toys and rebuild them into something new, in the same way that they could build and rebuild with their wooden bricks.

In 1906, using the experience he had gained while tinkering about in his workshop, and with his children's needs in mind, Hornby began to experiment with various shapes and sizes cut from pieces of metal. Eventually he developed his precision-made engineering system. Realising he had more than a toy for small boys, Hornby patented his invention and began to sell small boxes of components, which he called 'Mechanics Made Easy'. The following year, 1907, he changed the title to 'Meccano'.

Demand for his toy began to increase and on 4 July 1908 he officially registered his company of Meccano Limited. From those early beginnings, a complete Meccano system now contains more than 300 individual parts, some of which are electronic.

Hornby model railways and Dinky Toys were also the idea of Frank Hornby.

MOTHER'S DAY
Anna Jarvis · 1908

Although Mother's Day is celebrated on the fourth Sunday in Lent in Britain, it has nothing to do with Mothering Sunday, the age-old Christian festival — when it was the custom to visit the Mother Church — which falls on that particular day.

Mother's Day is a purely secular event thought up by

Anna Jarvis of Philadelphia. After Anna's mother died on 9 May 1905, Anna arranged an informal church service each year on the anniversary of her death. Eventually Anna decided that there ought to be a special day to honour all mothers. She wrote thousands of letters and campaigned public figures for her cause.

Finally, in 1908, her crusade brought the results she wanted — a special day for mothers. Then on 7 May 1914 a bill was introduced in Congress to set aside the second Sunday in May as national Mother's Day. The bill was passed unanimously and President Wilson signed the proclamation, stating that the Stars and Stripes, the American flag, should be flown on that day.

The idea soon spread to other countries, although the day is not always the same. In the United States of America it falls around 10 May, in France at the end of May. But it is in America where the greatest celebrations are held and Mother's Day is really big business.

Sadly, the lady who fought so hard for Mother's Day never became a mother herself. Anna Jarvis remained unmarried, and having frittered away a fortune of almost a $¼ million, she died blind and penniless in a Pennsylvania hospital.

NISSEN HUT
Peter Nissen · 1916

The Nissen hut was invented of necessity by Capt Peter Norman Nissen, an Army engineer, during World War I. When the British government introduced conscription in 1916, thousands of troops were drafted into the forces, many of them into the army to fight in the fields of France. Accommodation was scarce until Capt Nissen, Officer Commanding 29 Company RE, devised his temporary home — an inverted U-shaped hut, measuring 27ft × 15ft, and roofed with bent corrugated-iron sheets. The hut was lined with matchboard, and had a window at one end, and a door with windows on either side, at the other.

The Nissen hut, which won its inventor the DSO, was first erected at Hesdin, France in 1916.

Various other huts appeared as temporary accommodation during both world wars, but the Nissen has survived them all and is still used today for both military and civil purposes. And its basic design is unchanged.

In 1971 Nissen's 22-year-old grandson, Richard Nissen, designed a heavy-duty cardboard hut for use in disaster areas. The new Nissen, which can be erected in just over an hour, will last for about a year.

PAPER PATTERNS
Ebenezer Butterick · 1863

Ironically enough, the man who thought of using paper patterns for home-dressmaking was himself in business as a shirt-maker. But far from putting him out of business, his idea made him a fortune.

One day in 1863, Ebenezer Butterick, from Stirling in Massachusetts, thought that if he could design a pattern for a shirt, anyone could buy a copy and make the shirt at home. Butterick designed several styles, and these were in such demand that he decided to tackle children's clothes.

With his wife Ellen he designed a pattern for a child's outfit. Again this was successful, and the Buttericks then branched out into women's clothes. The easy-to-follow patterns were cut from white tissue paper, and wrapped in another sheet of paper which bore a picture of the finished garment and a set of simple instructions.

The sewing machine was becoming a popular acquisition and making clothes at home was becoming a new hobby, besides being money saving. Demand for the Buttericks' designs grew and in eight years they had sold 6 million patterns. Thirteen years after the first pattern was cut in Massachusetts, Butterick was an established international company with offices in London, Paris, Vienna and Berlin.

In the wake of Butterick's success, other paper-pattern companies were formed, and today home-dressmaking is tackled by enthusiasts throughout the world.

PARKING METER
Carlton Magee · 1933

In 1933 Carlton Magee, the editor of a newspaper in Oklahoma, became the chairman of a committee set up by a businessmen's association to enquire into ways of imposing stricter parking controls in the city. Magee decided on a parking meter that would both regulate the traffic and bring in a revenue to the city. He established the Dual Parking Meter Company to produce his two-R meters (Regulation and Revenue). The city fathers were well pleased with Magee's idea and they gave his company an order for 150 meters. And the first parking meters came into use on 16 July 1935.

In Britain the first parking meters appeared in July 1958 when 625 meters were installed by Westminster City Council in north-west Mayfair, in London.

PENDULUM
Galileo · 1583

To most people, perhaps, a pendulum is a simple device — a weight hooked on to a rod fixed to a clock to regulate the accuracy of the beat. But the pendulum was in fact one of the most important discoveries of Galileo, the Italian astronomer and scientist.

In 1583 nineteen-year-old Galileo was watching the swinging of the candelabrum in the cathedral at Pisa, where he was a university student, when he was struck by the fact that no matter what the range of the swings they were accomplished in equal times. To verify his belief, he timed the swings against his own pulse. Galileo concluded that the simple pendulum could be invaluable in the exact measurement of time. Sixty years later he used his discovery in the design of a clock.

In 1851 Jean Foucault, the French scientist, used the pendulum — a heavy iron ball suspended by a wire from the dome of the Panthéon in Paris — to demonstrate the first physical proof of the rotation of the earth.

Since Galileo's discovery the pendulum has been used in countless ways and, besides the clock, the most common is probably the metronome that beats time for music.

PERMANENT WAVING
Karl Ludwig Nessler · 1901

The first permanent wave was carried out in 1901 by Karl Nessler, the son of a Black Forest shoemaker. It had been hoped that Nessler would become a shoemaker like his father, but poor eyesight prevented him from coping with the small stitches of the cobbler's art. So he turned to hair dressing.

In Paris he learned the art of Marcel waving from Marcel Grateau. This method used heated tongs to produce a headful of waves and curls. But the tonged waves did not last long, and so Nessler devised his own method of a 'permanent' wave. His idea was to soak the hair with chemicals and then heat it in curlers. He tried it out on a client, but was instantly dismissed when his employer discovered how he was experimenting.

Nessler then opened his own salon and developed his 'permanent waving' machine. On 8 October 1906 he demonstrated his permanent wave before an audience of hair stylists at the salon in Oxford Street, London. Sadly the hairdressers were not enthusiastic about his idea. The machine he used was large and cumbersome and the long-suffering client was forced to wear heavy brass curlers, weighing about 25lb, for six hours.

But then came World War I and Nessler emigrated to the United States to avoid being interned as an alien. His luck turned, for in 1915 Irene Castle, the exhibition dancer, introduced the bobbed hairstyle to the nation, and permanent waving came into its own.

PETROL PUMP
Sylvanus Bowser · 1885

In 1885 Jake Gumper, an Indiana shopkeeper, was in danger of losing his customers. The trouble was that Gumper sold both butter and paraffin in his shop and the paraffin had leaked from its cask and impregnated the butter. Gumper's customers threatened to shop elsewhere if he did not mend his paraffin cask.

Gumper explained his difficulty to his friend, Sylvanus Bowser, who had the idea of making a pump for dispensing the paraffin away from the butter. Neither of them seemed to have had the simple idea of moving the paraffin cask to another part of the shop. But that was just as well for Bowser.

Bowser's contraption was a round tank with a metal cylinder inside it. A plunger inside the cylinder operated a valve that would open to let in a gallon of paraffin when the plunger was raised, and close when the plunger was lowered. Leading from the cylinder out through the tank was a tap through which the paraffin flowed.

Bowser not only saved Gumper's business, but he built up a flourishing business for himself to manufacture his brainchild. But it was twenty years before the pump was used for measuring fuel for motor cars. In 1905, S.F. Bowser & Co Inc introduced the first self-measuring petrol pump for car fuel at Fort Wayne in Indiana. Hand-operated pumps were installed in Britain in 1920, and in 1921 the first automatic pump, by Bowser, was used at a garage in Manchester.

PLASTICINE
William Harbutt · 1896

The easily mouldable clay was the brainwave of William Harbutt, an art teacher from Bath.

Harbutt realised that the clay his young students were using for sculpting was heavy and difficult to use. With the help of a friend, he mixed the clay with oil and water, rolled it flat with a garden roller to exude excess water, then squeezed it through a fine dye plate and left it to mature for a few weeks.

Harbutt named his new clay 'Plasticine' and patented his idea in about 1896.

PLIMSOLL LINE
Samuel Plimsoll · 1876

The set of lines painted on a ship to indicate the depth to which the ship may be safely loaded in varying waters and conditions was the idea of Samuel Plimsoll, the nineteenth-century British politician and reformer.

Plimsoll, who was known as the merchant seaman's friend, fought for better conditions for the seamen and in 1876 was instrumental in getting Disraeli's government to pass the Merchant Shipping Act, which introduced the safety measure.

POSTAGE STAMP
James Chalmers · 1840

The world's first adhesive postage stamp, the Penny Black bearing the head of Queen Victoria, was the idea of a Scottish printer named James Chalmers.

Early in 1840 Sir Rowland Hill, the social and administrative reformer, was looking for ways to reform the British postal system. Chalmers wrote to him and suggested that prepaid postage, by means of an adhesive stamp, would be cheaper than the existing method of collecting postage from the recipient when the letter was delivered. Under that system the cost of the postage depended upon how far the letter had to travel.

After studying the system, Rowland Hill discovered that the cost of conveying a letter was very small and bore little relation to the distance the letter had to travel. The cost mainly depended upon the number of letters conveyed. Hill decided that if the cost of sending a letter was reduced, more letters would be sent and the postage revenue would not decrease.

The penny post was introduced in May 1840 and within a few years the number of letters sent each year had reached 169 million — more than double the 82 million that were sent under the old system. Today the number has reached more than 10,000 million a year.

By 1860 Chalmers's idea of the adhesive postage stamp had been adopted by most countries throughout the world.

POTATO CRISPS
George Crum · 1853

Way back in the middle of the last century an Adirondack Indian Chief called George Crum was employed as head chef at Moon's, a smart hotel in Saratoga Springs, New York. Crum was proud of the food he served and was much offended when one evening in 1853 a guest returned his chipped potatoes to the kitchen complaining that they were too thick. The pernickety gentleman wanted them as fine as the matchstick thin *pommes frites* he had recently eaten on his first visit to Paris.

George Crum cooked some finer potatoes. But still the guest was not satisfied. He sent them back with the waiter, who told Crum: 'He says they're to be even thinner.'

In a fit of rage the deeply offended Crum sharpened up his kitchen knife. Furious, he snatched a huge potato and fiercely cut it into paper-thin slices which he angrily plunged into boiling fat. He then personally took the golden crisps into the dining-room and presented them to the waiting guest. Satisfied at last, the guest congratulated Crum, saying that they were delicious. The potato crisp was born — or the potato chip as it is called in America — and the following day Moon's added a new speciality, 'Saratoga Chips', to its menu.

Eventually George Crum set up his own restaurant in Saratoga Springs with Saratoga Chips as his speciality. Very soon his customers included the socialites of New York, who came to savour his delicacy.

Saratoga Chips retained their name until about the beginning of the twentieth century, when they became known simply as potato chips, or potato crisps.

PREPARATORY SCHOOL
Rev Dr John Pearson · 1810

Prep schools as we know them today were the idea of a nineteenth-century clergyman, Dr John Pearson, who established Temple Grove Seminary in 1810.

Temple Grove, formerly the country residence of the Victorian Prime Minister Lord Palmerston, stood in 20 acres of ground between Mortlake and Richmond in Surrey. Dr Pearson founded his school for boys between the ages of 7 and 14 solely to prepare them for public school — especially Eton. The objective of his Classical teachings was that the boys should 'daily experience those advantages which distinguish the polished gentleman from the rustic clown'. And the young gentlemen wore a uniform of top hat, long-tailed jacket and white pantaloons.

Dr Pearson was a tough taskmaster. He believed that in order for boys to grow into gentlemen they need tough discipline both inside and outside the classroom. Life was very austere and each day began with the boys having to swallow two large spoonfuls of sulphur and treacle.

Although Dr Pearson's Temple Grove was the first school to be founded specifically as a prep school, both Cheam in Surrey and Twyford in Berkshire, which also prepared boys for public school, were established before Temple Grove. But at that time both these schools took older boys as well whom they prepared for the universities.

PRESERVED FOOD
Nicolas Appert · 1795

In 1795, when Napoleon's army was marching across Europe, the French government offered a prize of 12,000 francs to anyone who could invent a process for preserving food for the troops. The money was won by Nicolas Appert, a French pastry-cook who worked in Paris.

Appert's idea was to pack food — meat, fruit and vegetables — into glass containers and cook them, then heat them in water at very high temperatures and seal them with layers of cork.

This preserving method soon spread to England where Peter Durand used steel containers as well as glass bottles. In 1811 two engineers, Brian Donkin and John Hall, bought Durand's idea of metal containers from him and opened the first canning factory, but using tin plate instead of steel. Food continued to be preserved by Appert's method until 1860 when Louis Pasteur, the French scientist, declared that simply sealing the can was not sufficient to kill any bacteria already in it and that sterilising was essential.

From those early days of supplying Napoleon's troops with food, the canning industry throughout the world now uses 175,000 million cans each year to preserve an infinite variety of food and drink.

PRESSURE COOKER
Denis Papin · 1679

In 1682 John Evelyn, the English diarist, wrote that he had eaten a meal cooked in 'one of Monsieur Denis Papin's Digesters, which even softened bones'.

Denis Papin, a French physicist, invented his 'New Digester', or pressure cooker, in 1679 while he was working at the Royal Society in London. It was a cast-iron pot with an airtight lid, in which food was cooked by pressurised steam being forced through it at about 250°F. This high temperature allowed the food to cook in about a quarter of the usual time. In the lid was a valve to prevent the pot exploding as pressure built up.

In 1680 Papin was made a Fellow of the Royal Society, and they asked him to write a book about his invention. In the book, which was published the following year, Papin claimed that 'the oldest and hardest cow beef may be made as tender and savoury as young and choice meat'. The society members then asked to taste food cooked in such a way, and in August 1682 they sat down to a meal prepared by Papin himself. The food lived up to Papin's claim as John Evelyn, who was among the society members, was able to testify.

After the excitement at the Royal Society, Papin's invention sank into comparative oblivion until the late nineteenth century, when small domestic pressure cookers became popular for making home preserves. Their popularity began to increase during World War I as food, which was rationed, went further and tasted better when cooked by pressure. In 1905 the Presto Company of Wisconsin manufactured the first aluminium cooker, and in 1938 Alfred Vischer, a Chicago draughtsman, designed the type of cooker that is used today — a long-handled pan with an interlocking lid, and an improved pressure-tight seal with a replaceable rubber sealing ring.

PRESSURE SUIT
August Siebe · 1837

The idea for the pressure suit came from a German mechanic, August Siebe, who designed an outfit for deep-sea divers in 1837.

The all-in-one suit was made of waterproofed canvas and had a heavy screw-on helmet.

RED CROSS
Henri Dunant · 1859

The worldwide organisation of the Red Cross stems from the ideal of one man — Henri Dunant, a Swiss banker and philanthropist.

In 1838, at the age of ten, Dunant was taken by his father, a voluntary prison officer, to visit a prison. Here he saw prisoners shackled together exercising in the yard and breaking stones along the road. The impression this left on him, and an interview he later had with Mrs Harriet Beecher Stowe, author of *Uncle Tom's Cabin*, made him determined to do something for convicts and slaves, and for all who were oppressed and deprived of their liberty.

On 24 June 1859, whilst on his way from Geneva to France, where he hoped to enlist the aid of Napoleon III for one of his charity plans in Algeria, Dunant witnessed the Battle of Solferino between the French and Austrian armies, one of the fiercest battles of the nineteenth century. Appalled by the lack of medical supplies and attention given to the wounded, Dunant decided a volunteer service had to be organised. He gathered together a number of women who tended the hundreds of wounded soldiers of all nationalities, and helped the hard-pressed surgeons as best they could.

From that battle Dunant determined to form a body of people who would rally together in times of war and attend to the needs of the wounded and dying. Dunant decreed that a suffering human being shall be helped for his own sake only, without regard to race, creed or political beliefs and irrespective of whether he is friend or foe.

He published a book on his experiences at Solferino, *Un Souvenir de Solferino*, which gained worldwide support for his idea. A Swiss lawyer, Gustave Moynier, impressed by what he had read in the book, approached Dunant and he, Dunant, and three others constituted a committee to form permanent relief societies in all countries. This was the beginning of the International Committee of the Red Cross in Geneva as it is today.

Napoleon III declared his support, and neutral status was accorded to ambulances, hospitals, wounded and field-hospital staffs. Other heads of European states supported him and on 22 August 1864 the first Geneva Convention was signed. This lays down that once a soldier is wounded he, and everyone and everything concerned with his protection, ceases to be an enemy. An emblem by which the relief workers could be recognised was devised and, as a tribute to Switzerland, this was the Swiss flag reversed — a red cross on a white ground. So was born the Red Cross. Only Florence Nightingale opposed the idea. She believed that care of the wounded should be undertaken by the government of the army concerned, and strongly disagreed with the idea of an international medical aide.

In 1901 Dunant was awarded a half share in the first ever Nobel Peace Prize. He died on 30 October 1910 at the age of 82.

RICKSHAW
Jonathan Scobie · 1860s

To be told that an American first thought up the idea of the rickshaw sounds as incongruous as being told that a Japanese invented baseball. But it was indeed an American who first conceived the idea.

During the 1860s Jonathan Scobie, a Baptist minister from Tennessee, was living in Yokohama, Japan, when his wife became physically handicapped. So that she would not be completely housebound, Scobie invented the two-wheeled, hooded carriage and used to take her with him on his ministerial visits. His parishioners, so impressed with his ingenuity, copied his idea and the rickshaw — or to give it its proper Japanese name, *Jinrickisha*, meaning man-powered carriage — soon became a popular means of transport throughout Japan.

ROLLER SKATES
Joseph Merlin · 1760

The first roller skates on record were constructed by Joseph Merlin, a Belgian musician, in 1760.

Merlin had been invited by the society hostess, Mrs Cornelly, to a masquerade at the elegant Carlisle House in London's Soho Square. Determined to cut a dash, he glided into the ballroom on his specially constructed wheeled shoes, playing his violin for added effect. But unfortunately for Merlin, he could neither brake, nor change direction — and unable to stop he zoomed at speed straight into an ornate, full-length looking-glass. The glass shattered to smithereens, the violin broke, and poor Merlin ended up severely injured in a heap amid the jagged shards of glass.

Needless to say, after that shattering introduction, roller skates did not catch on, and nothing more was heard of them for more than sixty years. Then in 1823, Robert John Tyers, a London fruiterer, built himself a pair with five small wheels arranged in a single line on each skate. He patented his 'Volitos' on 22 April 1823 as 'an apparatus to be attached to boots for the purpose of travelling or pleasure'. He then demonstrated them at the tennis-court in Windmill Street, Soho. This time skates did catch on, and later that year a public skating rink was opened in Windmill Street.

The first four-wheeled roller-skates were patented in New York by James L. Plimpton, in 1863. The prototype of today's skates, these had small boxwood wheels arranged in pairs and separated by rubber pads. On these skates balance could be maintained while intricate twists and turns were executed — and before long a skating craze had swept across America and into Europe.

SAFETY GLASS
Edouard Benedictus · 1904

In 1904 a French scientist named Edouard Benedictus was working in his Paris laboratory when he accidentally knocked an empty bottle off a shelf. The bottle hit the floor and smashed but, to Benedictus's surprise, the glass did not scatter and the bottle kept its shape. When Benedictus picked the bottle up, he saw that it had contained a collodion solution, which had evaporated and left a cellulose skin on the inside of the bottle; the skin had held the shattered pieces of glass together.

The idea for safety glass then came to Benedictus. He coated two sheets of flat glass with an adhesive and sandwiched them together over a sheet of cellulose nitrate. When struck, the glass simply cracked rather than shattered.

Safety glass was soon being used to make windscreens for motor cars and other vehicles. After the discovery of cellulose acetate plastic in 1929, the inner lining was replaced with plastic, since the cellulose nitrate sheet darkened to yellow in time.

Today safety glass is produced by heating the glass gently, then chilling the surface by a blast of air. If the glass breaks it shatters into granules rather than sharp splinters.

SAFETY-PIN
Walter Hunt · 1849

The age-old adage, 'Necessity is the mother of invention', was borne out in 1849 when Walter Hunt, a New York draughtsman, was asked to pay back 15 dollars he owed to a colleague.

Penniless, and with no chance of gathering the money quickly, Hunt sat at his drawing-board and doodled the idea for a safety-pin. He then took a length of wire and shaped it into a working model. All in the same day he patented the idea and sold the patent rights for 100 dollars. He was then able to honourably discharge his debt.

Like Mary Phelps Jacob, the inventor of the bras-
sière, (see page 10), Hunt received only his initial
payment for his patent rights, but his idea has made a
fortune for the manufacturers.

Hunt's inventive ability far exceeded his business
potential, for it was he who first thought of the
lock-stitch sewing machine. He had his brainwave in
the 1830s but refrained from patenting it because his
daughter thought it would put all the seamstresses out
of work. In 1854 Hunt decided to patent his idea, only
to find that Elias Howe had been granted the patent
eight years previously, having thought of the idea more
than a decade after Hunt.

SAFETY RAZOR
King Camp Gillette · 1901

In 1895 King Camp Gillette, a travelling salesman from
Wisconsin, was given a piece of advice by an inventor
friend: if you invent something that people can use and
throw away, they will come back for more and you will
be a rich man.

Some time later, Gillette remembered that advice.
While shaving one morning with his cut-throat razor he
realised that only a very small part of the blade was
ever used. Then he hit upon his idea — why not make
small blades that could be thrown away.

He designed a blade holder and, with a mechanic
friend, William Nickerson, he filed a patent in 1901 and
three years later began production of his razors in
Boston. At first business was slow, but by 1906 he had
sold 90,000 razors and over 12 million blades.

Gillette's safety razor spread throughout the world,
and his business went from strength to strength. In 1974
the Gillette company produced the disposable plastic
razor — a thing that people used and threw away and
then came back for more.

SALVATION ARMY
William Booth · 1878

In 1865 William Booth, a minister with the Methodist New Connexion, broke away from his church to start his own mission at Whitechapel in the east end of London. Booth, who was encouraged by his wife Catherine, wanted a less conventional approach to teaching Christianity to the poor working classes of the great cities. He was a charismatic preacher and very soon he had gathered together a band of workers and converts who were willing to follow him.

In 1878 he called his mission the Salvation Army and he became its General. He adopted the motto 'Through blood and fire', and planned his mission on military lines, with members wearing uniform. Discipline and loyalty were demanded of every officer and holiness of life was essential for every member.

Very soon the Army spread to many parts of the world, with the General in supreme command. To promote propagation, brass bands were set up to play martial music and they, together with open air meetings, became a familiar feature of street scenes throughout the world. Today the Army even has its own 'pop' group, known as the Joy Singers.

The Salvation Army, which was set up to bring life and hope to the drunkards and outcasts of Victorian London, now has millions of members carrying out a multitude of tasks, both spiritual and social.

SEED-DRILL
Jethro Tull · 1701

The idea for the seed-drill came from the English agriculturist, Jethro Tull, in 1701. Tull was originally a lawyer, but turned to agriculture with the coming of the enclosure system, which encouraged more scientific methods of farming.

Before Tull's invention seed had always been sown by hand and much of it was scattered in a careless and wasteful way. With the seed-drill, seeds were fed evenly through a tube and into a furrow made by a coulter, or blade. The furrows were in straight lines that allowed for weeding between the rows. With this method crop yields improved considerably.

Many of today's seed-drills work on the same principle as Tull's original idea, the improvement being a mechanism to control the amount of seed dropped.

Ever in search of farming improvement, Tull spent many months touring Europe, where he learned the value of the cultivator in aerating the soil. He introduced the horse-hoe into his own farming methods, the practice of which he explained in his book, the alliteratively titled, *Horse-hoeing Husbandry*.

SEMAPHORE
Claude Chappe · 1793

Semaphore, the arm-signalling method of sending messages, was invented in 1793 by Claude Chappe, a French engineer and clergyman.

Chappe devised the word 'telegraph' for his system, from the Greek words 'far off' and 'to write', and after giving a demonstration which was seen by Robespierre and other revolutionary leaders, he proposed that his system should be used for carrying war messages.

The first line was set up between Paris and Lille, a distance of more than 140 miles, in 1794. Mechanical arms, like railway signals, on top of high towers sent the messages. When human beings were used to send messages they used flags, one held in each hand. Very soon Chappe's signalling idea spread abroad and by 1796 Britain had a signalling system between London and the coastal ports.

Although semaphore was superseded by the electric telegraph, it is still used at sea.

SEWING MACHINE
Balthazar Krems · 1810

Although various types of sewing machine were patented during the nineteenth century, the idea came from a German sock maker called Balthazar Krems, in 1810.

Krems's invention was a chain-stitch machine. When the handle was turned the needle, which had a hole near its point, rose and fell to feed a thread through the fabric in a series of connecting loops like a chain.

Unfortunately, Krems's idea did not catch on. Then, in 1830, Barthelemy Thimmonier, a tailor from the French village of St Etienne, devised a similar chain-stitch machine. This was successful and Thimmonier built eighty machines and opened a factory to make uniforms for the Revolutionary French army. But other tailors, fearing his new-fangled idea would ruin their livelihood, rioted and destroyed them all.

In 1833 the American inventor of the safety-pin (see page 44), Walter Hunt, built a lock-stitch machine which he sold to George Arrowsmith, a New York manufacturer. But lack of money prevented Arrowsmith from developing it. Then in 1845 Elias Howe, a machinist from Boston, Massachusetts, invented another lock-stitch machine. More machines appeared throughout America until, in 1851, Isaac Singer, a mechanic from New York, invented a lock-stitch machine worked by a treadle. Singer's idea was immediately successful. He opened factories in America and Europe to build his machine which, by the time he died in 1875, had made him a multimillionaire.

Modern sewing machines are controlled by silicon chips and can perform any needlework task that can be done by hand.

STAMP COLLECTING
Stanley Gibbons · 1856

Although records show that a man named John Tom-lynson began collecting stamps on 7 May 1840, the day after the introduction of the Penny Black, the man who introduced stamp collecting to millions was Stanley Gibbons, the son of a Plymouth chemist. And coincidentally Gibbons was born in the same year in which the Penny Black, the world's first adhesive postage stamp, was produced.

Gibbons had been collecting stamps from childhood, and his business began in 1856 at a small desk in his father's chemist shop where he would pursue his hobby with interested customers. Gibbons preferred philately to pharmaceuticals and when he inherited the business from his father he sold the pharmacy and concentrated on stamps.

In 1863, he took a gamble and paid £5 for a kitbagful of stamps brought in by two sailors who had won them in a raffle in Cape Town. That chance purchase was the beginning of the Stanley Gibbons empire, for the stamps were all Cape Triangulars, which made Gibbons a profit of £500.

Gibbons then began to import stamps from all over the world, and again fortune smiled on him. A £20 order he had placed for unused stamps from Albany in Western Australia contained 120 2d stamps for which he had had to pay 6d each since they were wrongly printed in the colour of the 6d issue. But those stamps — the rare mauve 2d stamps of 1879 — are now priced at more than £3,000 each in the Gibbons catalogue.

In 1870, Gibbons published his first catalogue and his first stamp album, and in 1874 he moved the business to London. In 1890 he sold out to Charles Phillips, a stamp dealer from Birmingham, for £25,000. The company still bears Gibbons's name, and is now the philatelic centre of the world.

STETHOSCOPE
René Laennec · 1815

Little children playing on a fallen tree in a French park in 1815 inspired a young physician, René Laennec, to invent the stethoscope.

Laennec watched as some of the children scraped one end of the trunk, while others listened at the other end. The scraping noise carried loud and clear along the trunk. The idea then came to Laennec that he could use this method of amplified sound in his work as a doctor.

First he rolled a piece of paper into a tube and placed one end against a friend's chest, and the other to his own ear. He could hear the heartbeat very distinctly.

He improved on this prototype by making a wooden tube, 10in long and ¾in across, with a hole in the middle. By placing one end of the tube against a patient's chest, and the other to his ear, he could hear the heartbeat and the flow of air in and out of the lungs. This stethoscope was first used at the Hôpital Necker in Paris.

Improvements on this wooden instrument continued to be made and by the end of the nineteenth century the familiar rubber stethoscope that we know today was devised.

SUBMARINE
Cornelius Drebbel · 1620

Although submersible craft are said to have been used by Alexander the Great at the siege of Tyre in 322 BC, the first known submarine was the idea of a Dutchman named Cornelius Drebbel.

Drebbel, who was working in England at the court of James I, built his craft — a twelve-man rowing boat, propelled by oars protruding through sealed portholes, and covered with a leather waterproof skin — in 1620 and tried it out on the Thames. Unfortunately for Drebbel, his craft could not remain watertight under submersion, and consequently the idea was rejected by the Admiralty.

In 1776, a century and a half after Drebbel's invention, an American engineer, David Bushnell, designed a workable submarine, the wooden *Turtle*, which was used during the American War of Independence. This was the forerunner of the modern craft. The *Turtle*, which was driven by cranking a propeller, had its buoyancy tanks flooded for submerging, and pumped out for surfacing. Its weapon was an explosive charge designed to 'screw' into an enemy ship.

In 1800 another American engineer, Robert Fulton, built the *Nautilus*, but this was rejected by both Napoleon and the British Admiralty as being too slow.

Next came the *H.L. Hunley* in 1863. This was an iron boiler converted by the Confederate Horace Hunley during the American Civil War. More sophisticated designs were developed over the years, and in 1958 the United States demonstrated the first nuclear-powered submarine — another *Nautilus*.

SUPERMARKET SHOPPING CART
Sylvan Goldman · 1937

When supermarkets first opened in Britain in the 1940s, shopping carts came with them and were taken for granted. But that was not so in the early days of supermarket shopping in America. There shoppers had to be content with the arm-breaking hand baskets overflowing their capacity.

What grieved Sylvan Goldman, owner of two supermarket chains in Oklahoma, was not so much the plight of the shopper, as the fact that he was missing out on sales which were limited by the size of the little baskets. Offering shoppers a second basket at the check-out when the first was full, increased sales a little, but not enough for Goldman, for there was a limit to how many times a shopper would go round the store.

Then Goldman had an idea that he thought would revolutionise shopping and send his sales rocketing. One night, as he was brooding over low takings, he suddenly thought of the folding chairs that salesmen used when they called on him. He thought that if he put wheels on the legs of the chairs and raised the seats, he could put one basket on each seat and one below, and his customers could use two baskets at once. When the carts were not in use they would fold up for storage at the front of the store.

Goldman had about fifty chairs converted into carts and then put an advertisement in the *Oklahoma City Times* announcing 'a new, sensational revelation in food buying' in the hope of attracting masses of customers. But when he went into the store on the morning of 4 June 1937, the day of the innovation, no one was using the carts. Undaunted, Goldman placed another advertisement which said, 'Shoppers came, saw, and said "It's a wow!"' — 'the biggest lie I ever told' he confessed. Goldman then hired actors and actresses to push carts throughout the store all day, hoping that genuine shoppers would follow suit, which they eventually did.

The shopping cart caught on to such an extent that there are now 1½ million being made every year, and almost 25 million being used throughout the world. One of Goldman's originals is preserved for posterity as part of American cultural history in the Smithsonian Institution in Washington.

When asked, at the age of eighty, if the cart had made him rich, Goldman replied: 'It didn't make me poor.'

TEDDY BEAR
Morris Michtom · 1902

Perhaps the world's favourite toy is the Teddy Bear, and this little creature came into existence because of the soft heartedness of a President of the United States of America.

In November 1902 President Theodore Roosevelt was out bear hunting in Mississippi, where he had gone to help settle that state's border dispute with Louisiana, when a frisky bear cub wandered into his rifle sights. The kindly Roosevelt could not pull his gun on the little creature, who escaped, unknowingly, into immortality.

The incident inspired Clifford Berryman, a Washington cartoonist, to recapture the moment in a cartoon, which he entitled 'Drawing the Line in Mississippi'.

The cartoon, which appeared in many newspapers, was seen by a Russian immigrant named Morris Michtom, who owned a sweetshop in Brooklyn. Michtom straightaway made a toy bear from brown plush and gave it movable arms and button eyes. He put it in his shop window along with the cartoon and a label reading: 'Teddy's Bear'. He then wrote to President Roosevelt asking if he could use the name Teddy as a trademark.

In a handwritten reply, Roosevelt told Michtom, 'I don't think my name is worth much in the toy bear cub business, but you are welcome to use it.'

Little did he know what his bear and his name were destined for.

TELEPHONE
Johann Philipp Reis · 1860

Although the telephone as we know it today was invented by the Scottish scientist, Alexander Graham Bell, the idea came from the German inventor, Johann Philipp Reis, who was born at Gelnhausen in Cassel.

Reis's telephone, which he made in 1860 (or 1861) was a crude construction that transmitted noise and music only, and not the human voice. It was not until 1876 that Alexander Graham Bell hit upon his invention of a device for transmitting and receiving speech.

Bell, a professor of Vocal Physiology at Boston University, whose special interest was teaching the deaf, was trying to invent a machine which would enable deaf people to 'hear' by means of electrical sound vibrations. He sat for hours experimenting with a metal diaphragm placed next to a coil that was wound round a magnet. During one of his experiments, Bell spilt some acid on to his clothes. He immediately called out to his assistant, Thomas Watson, who was in a room below, listening for the vibrations: 'Mr Watson. Come here. I want you.' Watson heard Bell's voice over the telephone receiver and rushed to help. Quite accidentally, Bell had invented the telephone and made the first telephone call.

Bell then patented his 'electrical speech' machine, and later that year gave his first public demonstration at the centennial exposition in Philadelphia which marked the 100th anniversary of American Independence.

TIME SWITCH
Walter Christopher Thurgar · 1867

Time switches were first used in the streets of Norwich during the nineteenth century to turn the street lights on and off at pre-set times.

The idea for the clockwork device, which had to be wound once a week, came from Walter Christopher Thurgar, a Norwich surgeon, who patented his invention in 1867.

THE TIMES
John Walter · 1785

The Times newspaper was founded in 1785 by John Walter, a coal merchant turned underwriter, who had acquired a printing company the previous year.

Walter originally called his paper the *Daily Universal Register*, but changed its name to *The Times* in 1788. Soon it was nicknamed *The Thunderer*, a name which stuck for many years.

TOILET PAPER
Joseph Gayetty · 1857

Toilet paper was the idea of an American salesman, Joseph Gayetty of New York.

Gayetty sold his product under the name 'Gayetty's Medicated Paper' in 1857. It was made from grey-coloured manilla hemp paper and was watermarked with Gayetty's name.

He advertised it as 'a pure article for the toilet, and a prevention for piles'.

TOOTHBRUSH
William Addis · 1780

A London tanner, William Addis, first thought up the idea for the toothbrush in 1780.

The company he formed to commercialise his invention now manufactures a variety of brushes and other home utensils.

TRAFFIC ISLANDS
John Hastings · 1860

During the latter half of the nineteenth century, a saddler named John Hastings kept a shop on a dangerous corner of a busy street in Liverpool. From this vantage point, Hastings could see that people needed help in crossing the road. And he hit upon the idea of pedestrian refuges in the middle of the street.

In 1860 he put forward his idea to the City Fathers, but it was rejected by both the City Council and the Police. Then the following year, a prominent business-man, stationer John Walmsley, was killed instantly when he was knocked down by a bus on the exact spot that John Hastings had warned about.

After the fatality, Hastings's idea of refuges was reconsidered, and in 1862, two years after Hastings suggested the idea, six traffic islands were installed in various streets of Liverpool. Lamp-posts were erected on the islands to light them at night.

Two years later, in 1864, a Col Pierpoint privately installed the first traffic island in London. Pierpoint paid for the refuge himself so that he could safely cross the road to and from his club in St James without fear of accident. Safe though the colonel was when standing on his refuge, pride in his island caused him to glance admiringly over his shoulder as he approached the kerb. And one day, during a backward glance, he walked into the path of a cab.

VACUUM CLEANER
H. Cecil Booth · 1901

In 1901 Hubert Cecil Booth, an English engineer, was invited to St Pancras Station in London to watch an American demonstrating his new railway carriage cleaner. The cleaner removed the dust from the carriage by blowing it into a container. But Booth was not impressed as most of the dust missed the container and was blown all over the place. Booth decided that the answer was to suck the dust into a container, not to blow it. To prove his theory to scornful friends, Booth spread a handkerchief over the arm of his chair and sucked hard, drawing out a large patch of dust on to the handkerchief.

His theory proved, he set about building a suction cleaning machine. It consisted of an electrically driven pump, called a Puffing Billy, which sucked air along a hose and through a cloth filter. Booth patented his idea in August 1901, and set up the Vacuum Cleaner Company. He did not sell his cleaner at first, but mounted it on a horse-drawn cart and offered his services to householders. The pump remained outside the house on the cart, while the 100ft-long hose was passed through the window to do the cleaning inside.

In 1902 Booth cleaned the coronation carpet under the throne in Westminster Abbey in preparation for the crowning of Edward VII. Later the King commanded Booth to take the machine to Buckingham Palace and give a demonstration so that he and Queen Alexandra could see it working.

In 1906 Booth developed a smaller cleaning machine for domestic use, but this was still very heavy. The following year, an American named Murray Spangler designed a lighter machine, which he sold to William Hoover, who at that time was a leather manufacturer.

In 1913 Axel Wenner-Gren, a Swedish engineer working with the Aktiebolaget Elektrolux Company in Stockholm, developed the horizontal vacuum cleaner.

Since that demonstration in 1901, when Booth decided the answer was to suck, not blow the dust, millions of cleaners have been manufactured throughout the world each year.

VASELINE
Robert Chesebrough · 1859

In 1859 a young research chemist named Robert Chesebrough from Booklyn, New York, visited America's first oil-producing well in Titusville, Pennsylvania. There he became intensely interested in rod wax, the colourless residue that formed around the pump rods.

Chesebrough took a keg of the substance back to his laboratory and began experimenting. Eventually he discovered a way of extracting the wax, which he called petroleum jelly, from crude oil. Believing that his new product had healing powers, he inflicted various wounds and burns on his body and treated them with his soothing balm. Immediately they began to feel better.

Chesebrough then set about marketing his product. At first no one was interested in it as they thought it might explode, so Chesebrough travelled around America in an open car giving away free samples to anyone who would accept one. Very soon orders were pouring in for his now-famous discovery.

Vaseline, as he named it, soon began to be used for a

multitude of purposes, from supplying tears for Hollywood actresses to baiting fish hooks. And to prove its real worth, Chesebrough swallowed a teaspoonful each morning in the belief that it aided health and longevity. When he died in 1933 he was aged ninety-six.

Two stories attach to the brand name, Vaseline. One is said to stem from Chesebrough's wife who kept the scientist's laboratory supplied with fresh flowers each day. But her task was made increasingly difficult because Chesebrough would remove the flowers and use the vase for storing his petroleum jelly. When it came to naming the stuff, she suggested 'Vase-line' ('line' being a common attachment to names for American patent medicines in the nineteenth century).

The other theory is that Chesebrough, who believed that crude oil was formed by the hydrogen from decomposed water in the earth uniting with carbon, simply adapted the German word for water (*wasser*) and the Greek word for olive oil (*elaion*), and coined the anglicised word Vaseline.

WATER CLOSET
Sir John Harington · 1589

Although archaeologists' excavations have shown that the ancient Greeks, Romans and Egyptians built themselves lavatories of some kind, it was not until 1589 that the first flushing water closet was invented. The inventor was John Harington, a godson of Elizabeth I.

In 1584 Harington had been banished from Elizabeth's court for circulating a risqué story among the ladies of her bedchamber. During his five-year exile he retired to Kelston, near Bath, where he built himself a house and installed his flushing lavatory, which he recommended should be flushed at least once, preferably twice, a day. In 1591, the Queen forgave Harington and restored him to favour. She then visited Kelston, and was so impressed with Harington's invention that she commanded him to design one for her own personal use in Richmond Palace.

Harington called his lavatory 'Ajax' (from 'a jakes', an old word for privy). In 1596 he wrote a book, *The*

Metamorphosis of Ajax, which explained the workings of his invention.

Harington's invention went unsung for almost two hundred years — until 1775, when Alexander Cummings, a London watchmaker, invented another water closet that was more widely accepted. In 1889 Davis Bostel, a plumber from Brighton, improved on earlier designs and produced a water closet that was the forerunner of the modern system.

WIRE COAT-HANGER
Albert J. Parkhouse · 1903

Like many an invention before it, the wire coat-hanger sprang from the spur of the moment. Its inventor, Albert J. Parkhouse, was employed at the Timberlake Wire and Novelty Company in Jackson, Michigan, where he made lampshade frames and various other wire components. One day, in 1903, when Parkhouse returned from lunch, he found that the few hooks that the company provided for the men to hang their coats on had all been taken. There was nowhere for Parkhouse's coat except the floor, where a few other crumpled specimens lay. That did not please Parkhouse. In a fit of fury, he snatched a piece of wire, bent it into a coat-width shape, with a hook at the top, and hung his coat up on a cupboard.

When his employer saw what he had done, he immediately seized the idea and patented it, and from then on began to manufacture wire coat-hangers.

Parkhouse, the ingenious inventor, received nothing for his idea and continued to work at the wire factory.

WOMEN'S MAGAZINE
John Dunton · 1693

Women's magazines began as a 'problem page' almost three hundred years ago, and the agony aunt was a London bookseller named John Dunton. On 27 June 1693, Dunton published the first edition of *The Ladies' Mercury*, a single sheet printed on both sides, designed to tackle the hidden worries of late-seventeenth-century woman.

In his first edition Dunton invited ladies to 'send in their questions to the Latin Coffee House in Ave Maria Lane', and vowed that he would supply answers to 'all the nice and curious questions concerning love, marriage behaviour, dress and honour of the female sex, whether virgins, wives or widows'. And he promised to do so 'with zeal and softness becoming the sex'.

Dunton did not shy away from questions about adultery and fornication — neither did his readers. And both questions and answers were approached with unabashed forthrightness and honesty.

Dunton's bold approach set the style for future problem pages, which became an essential feature of all future women's magazines, until the late eighteenth century, when they fell into disrepute for about a hundred years. Then in 1852 the feature was revived, but in a very discreet form, by Samuel Beeton — husband of cookery expert Mrs Beeton — who introduced 'Cupid's Letter Bag' in his *Englishwomen's Domestic Magazine*, the first mass-circulation women's magazine aimed at the middle-class English housewife.

The first women's magazine to be edited by a woman was *The Female Tatler*, which was also the first to carry a variety of topics. It was first published in July 1709 by a Mrs Crackenthorpe, the pseudonym of the notorious Mary de la Rivière Manley, who in October of the same year was arrested for libel for publishing the scandalous *Secret Memoires and Manners of Several Persons of Quality*. Mrs Crackenthorpe also published intimate revelations of the famous in her magazine and consequently it was indicted as 'a nuisance' by a Grand Jury. Subsequent issues were so 'uninteresting' that the magazine lost its popularity.

X-RAYS
Wilhelm Röntgen · 1895

No one was more surprised at the discovery of X-rays than the discoverer himself. For, like many a good invention, they were discovered quite by accident. In November 1895 Wilhelm Röntgen, a Professor of Physics at Würzburg University in Bavaria, was experimenting with a cathode-ray tube in his laboratory when he suddenly saw a green light coming from a piece of cardboard across the room. The cardboard was covered with a chemical that glowed when light struck it. This puzzled Röntgen, for he was working in a darkened laboratory. He switched off the cathode-ray tube and the light disappeared. Röntgen then switched the tube on again and held his hand in front of the cardboard. He could hardly believe what he saw, for there, to his utter amazement, was not just the shadow of his hand but a clear picture of the bones inside.

Röntgen had no idea what the rays were so he simply called them X-rays. 'X', as he explained, 'being the mathematical symbol for an unknown quantity'.

Röntgen's discovery meant that doctors could examine patients internally without cutting them open.

Although his discovery was a milestone in the history of medicine, Röntgen refused to patent the X-ray, and he made not a penny out of its use.

ZIP-FASTENER
Whitcomb Judson · 1891

The zip-fastener was the brainchild of a Chicago engineer named Whitcomb Judson. Judson's original fastener, which he patented in 1891, was a shoe fastener called a 'Clasp-Locker or Unlocker', and it consisted of rows of hooks and eyes which were locked together by a slide. Two years later Judson devised another fastener consisting of interlocking teeth, designed for use on fabric and clothing, which he manufactured under the trade name of C-curity.

Neither of these fasteners was reliable since they would frequently burst open, and the machine on which they were produced frequently broke down.

Then in 1906 a Swedish engineer named Gideon Sundback, who was working for Judson in America, improved on the invention and produced a fastener with a series of cups behind the interlocking metal teeth that allowed the teeth to lock more securely when drawn together with a slide. In 1913 Sundback developed a machine that stamped out the metal teeth on to fabric tape, so producing the zip-fastener as we know it today.

One of the first uses of the zip-fastener was on a waterproof shoe known as a 'zipper' — and so the zip-fastener got its name.

INDEX